Mason & Matthew,

God Bless!

Gary Hayes

John 10:11

The Good Shepherd

Written and Illustrated by Gary Varvel

Dedicated to the memory of Forest E. Varvel

Printed in the U.S. All rights reserved.
Any unauthorized publication or use is strictly prohibited without written permission from the publisher.

ISBN: 978-0-692-314583-8

Copyright © 2014
Published by House of Grace Films, Inc.
7950 N County Road 650 E, Brownsburg, IN 46112
info@houseofgracefilms.org

www.thewarwithinmovie.com
www.houseofgracefilms.org
www.facebook.com/twwmovie

Once there was a good Shepherd who cared for his sheep.
He watched over them when they were awake or asleep.

He led them to green pastures
and to cool waters when they thirst.
He led them to shade when the sun's heat was the worst.

4

He led his sheep through the desert and the winter snow.

He even led them where they didn't want to go.

5

The good Shepherd said,
"Just follow me. I'm your best friend.
I will lead you to a place
where life will never end."

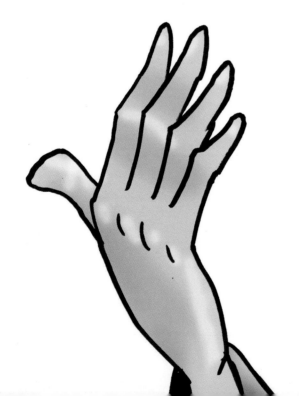

But one sheep loved the world and just wanted to play.
So she stopped following the good Shepherd
and just wandered away.

She went on a trip to see what she could find.
And her little baby lamb followed her close behind.

They climbed to the top of a great big hill.
The scene was so pretty, it gave them a thrill.
Then suddenly in the thicket, the sheep heard a sound,
Where the eyes of a snake looked up from the ground.

9

Without the good Shepherd,
they both were scared stiff.

Then the little lamb stumbled
and fell off the cliff.

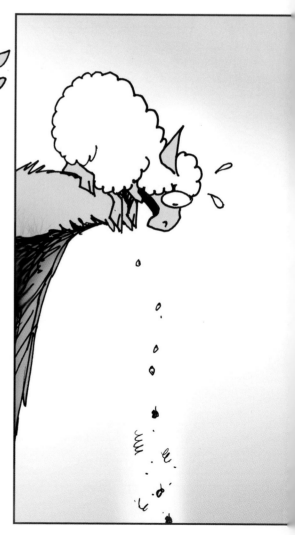

10

The mother sheep ran
to the bottom of the hill.

She cried and cried
as her baby laid still.

Then the snake slithered down
toward the lamb that was dead,
But the good Shepherd appeared
and crushed the snake's head.

Then he picked up and held the lamb that had died,
And hurried off with her mother close by his side.

13

He carried the lamb's body
to a fast-moving stream.
Then crossed over the water
as if in a dream.

When He stepped onto the shore, He gave a command.
Then the lamb sprang to life and danced in the new land.

The lamb's mother
bowed her head and cried.
She was sorry for not staying
close to the good Shepherd's side.

"Please forgive me," she said,
"I shouldn't have strayed."
Then the good Shepherd replied,
"Your debt has been paid."

16

As sure as the sun rises
and crosses the sky
All things that have life
sooner or later will die.

But only the good Shepherd
can take us to the place
Where life never ends
and we see Him face to face.

The Good Shepherd's Invitation

The Bible says that we are all "like sheep have gone astray; we have turned, every one, to his own way…" (Isaiah 53:6). That means that every person has wandered away from God and has broken His laws. Have you ever told a lie? Ever disobeyed your parents? Has there been a time when you took something that didn't belong to you? Who hasn't done things like this? That is called *sin* and punishment for sin is death in a place called *hell* (Romans 6:23a). That is bad news.

But here is the good news. Jesus says, "I am the Good Shepherd. The Good Shepherd gives His life for the sheep" (John 10:11). The Bible tells us that Jesus gave His life by dying on a cross for our sins. He rose again to life on the third day and offers the gift of eternal life to anyone who repents and believes in Him.

Jesus not only died for your sins to save you from hell; He is also offering you a gift of "eternal life." That is the most important gift you can own. So how do you receive His gift of "eternal life?" The Bible says, "If you confess with your mouth the Lord Jesus and believe in your heart that God has raised Him from the dead, you will be saved" (Romans 10:9). When you realize that you are a sinner, ask forgiveness for your sins, and believe that Jesus Christ is Who He said He is (Savior and Lord), then He will give you eternal life.

In Romans 10:13, the Bible says, "Whoever calls on the name of the Lord will be saved." Pray to the Lord, the Good Shepherd, today! Ask Him to forgive you for your sins and save you from hell. Tell Him that you believe in Him. **Do it today!**

Drawing by Ellie Sinclair (Ellie Henry) in the movie, *The War Within*.